and the
Slithery
Serpent

John Lomas-Bullivant

Chief Engineer Samson

Slithery Serpent

Captain Mack

Grabby Crabby

The Mayor

Marty Meddler

Tracy Trickster

Peter Patent

Yolanda Yummy

Dr Kwack

Daisy Digger

For Talie, Patrick and Nadine,
love you. Dad x – JLB

First published 2011 by Walker Books Ltd
87 Vauxhall Walk, London SE11 5HJ

2 4 6 8 10 9 7 5 3 1

This book has been typeset in Kronica Regular

Printed and bound in China

British Library Cataloguing in Publication Data:
a catalogue record for this book is available from the British Library

ISBN 978-1-4063-2364-1

www.walker.co.uk

www.captainmack.co.uk

Captain Mack must act fast to save the pilots!